The Drover's Dream

The Drover's Dream

Illustrated by
Deborah Niland

FONTANA PICTURE LIONS
Collins Australia

Illustrations © Deborah Niland 1979
First published 1979 by William Collins
Publishers Pty Ltd, Sydney
Reprinted 1981
First published in paperback 1981
Reprinted September 1981, 1984, 1985, 1987
Text set by Savage & Co. Pty Ltd, Brisbane
Printed by Dai Nippon Co. (Hong Kong) Ltd

National Library of Australia
Cataloguing in Publication data
The drover's dream
For children
ISBN 0 00 184386 9 (Hardback)
ISBN 0 00 661586 4 (Paperback)
I. Niland, Deborah, illus.
A821'.1

One night when travelling sheep,
  my companions lay asleep,
There was not a star to 'luminate the sky,

I was dreaming I suppose, for my eyes were partly closed,
When a very strange procession passed me by.

First there came a kangaroo
   with his swag of blankets blue,
A dingo ran beside him as his mate;
They were travelling mighty fast,
   but they shouted as they passed,
"We'll have to jog along, it's getting late!"

The pelican and the crane they came in from off the plain
To amuse the company with a Highland Fling;

The dear old bandicoot played
the tune upon his flute,

And the native bears sat round them in a ring.

The drongo and the crow sang us songs of long ago,
The frill-necked lizard listened with a smile,

And the emu standing near with his claw up to his ear
Said: "Funniest thing I've heard for quite a while!"

NORTH COTTESLOE
PRIMARY SCHOOL

The frogs from out the swamp where the
atmosphere is damp

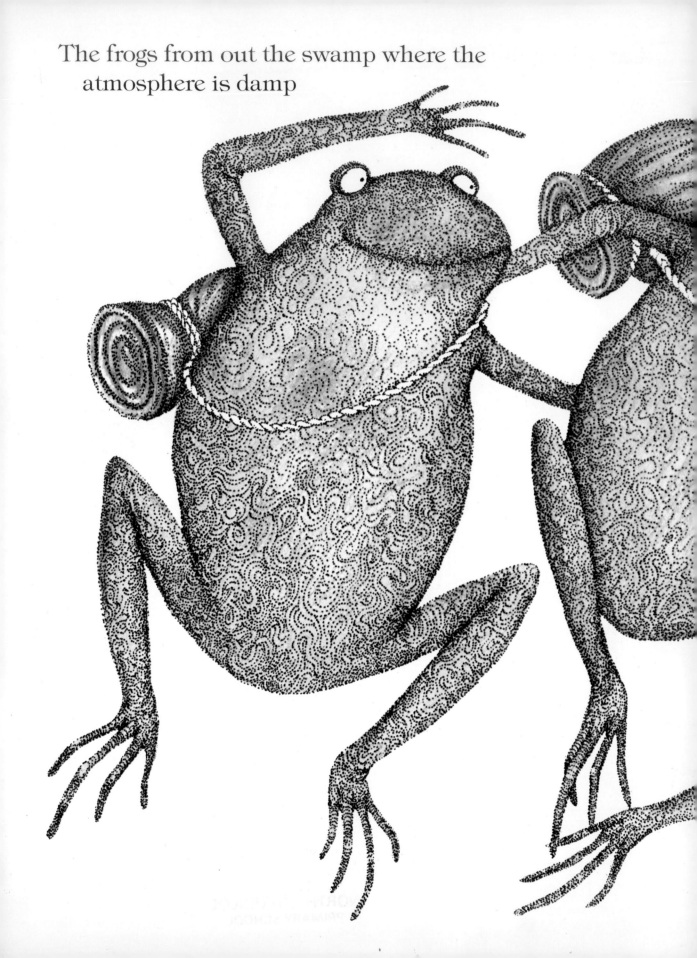

Came bounding in and sat upon the stones.

They each unrolled their swags,
    and produced from little bags
The violin, the banjo and the bones.

The goanna and the snake and the adder wide awake
With an alligator danced The Soldier's Joy.

In the spreading silky-oak the jackass cracked a joke,
And the magpie sang The Wild Colonial· Boy.

Some brolgas darted out from the tea-tree all about,
And performed a set of Lancers very well.

Then the parrot green and blue gave the orchestra its cue

To strike up The Old Log Cabin in the Dell.

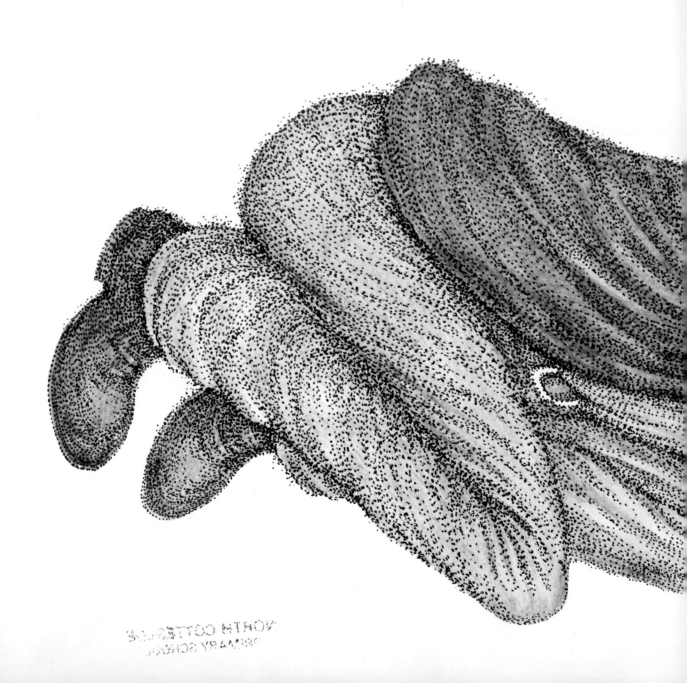

I was dreaming I suppose, of those entertaining shows,
But it never crossed my mind I was asleep,

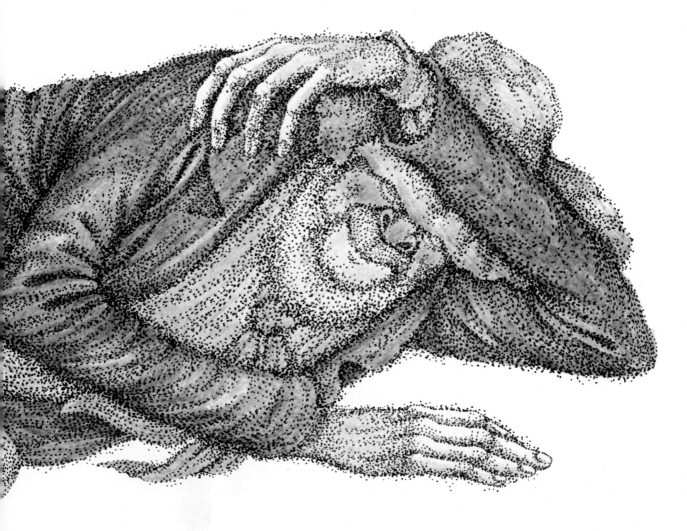

Till the boss beneath the cart woke me up with such a start
Yelling: "Dreamy, where the hell are all the sheep?"